SPLIT SCORES

In this league, bowling splits score high points. Each ball contains enough letters to make two words of four letters each. In every frame, fill in each pin with a new word, crossing off each letter in the ball as you use it. Though the first one is done, if you get the other seven, you'll have scored a perfect split.

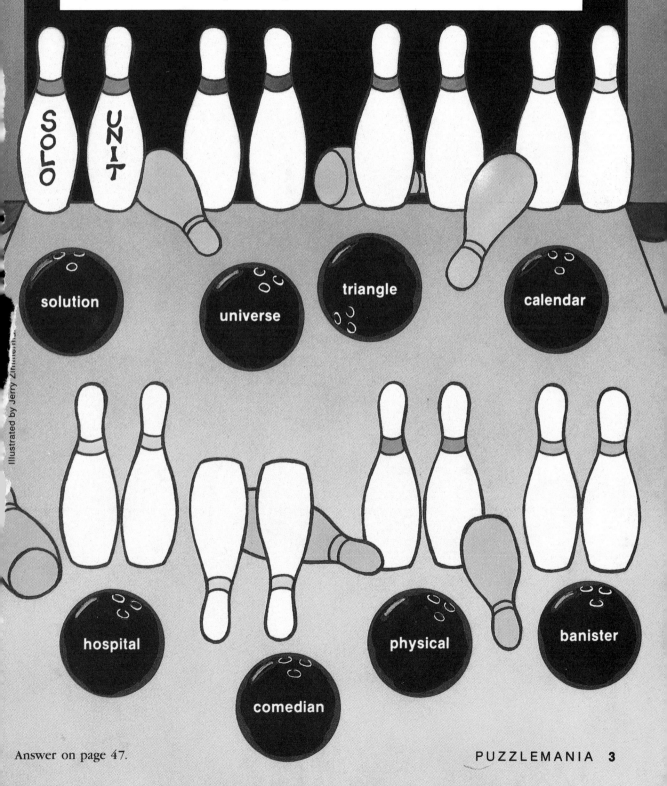

FOOD FIGHT

Duck! One pair of clowns, one pair of customers, and one pair of pies each match exactly. Can you find the matching pairs before getting hit in the face with a cream custard special? Watch out!

Answer on page 47.

Basso

4

ROW, ROW, ROW

Each flower has something in common with the two others in the same row. For example, all three flowers in the top row across have six petals. Look at the other rows across, down, and diagonally. What's the same about each row of three?

Answer on page 47.

Illustrated by Terry Rogers

ACT YOUR AGE

You don't have to be ancient to see that each word contains the letters AGE. If you manage to use the clues to fill in the missing letters and finish the words, you must be sage, indeed.

1. The one this puzzle appears on is number 7: *P* age

2. A place for a pet parakeet or rabbit: *C* age

3. Actors perform on this: *St* age

4. Reflection in a mirror: __ __ age

5. A place to park the car overnight: __ __ __ age

6. Trash: __ __ __ __ age

7. Something to put on a wound: __ __ __ __ age

8. Leafy vegetable, like lettuce: __ __ __ __ __ age

9. The distance a car drives: *Mil* age

10. Bravery: __ __ __ __ age

11. Suitcases for travel: __ __ __ __ age

12. German, English, Russian, or Spanish is one of these: __ __ __ __ __ age

Illustrated by Gregg Valley

HOSPITAL HAPPENINGS

Hospitals are big places that may look confusing because so many things are going on. But a hospital is easier to understand if you look at individual parts of it. All the words below have something to do with a hospital. Can you fit each word into the boxes on the grid? Use the size of each word as a clue to where it might go, and cross each word off the list once you find a spot for it. One is done for you.

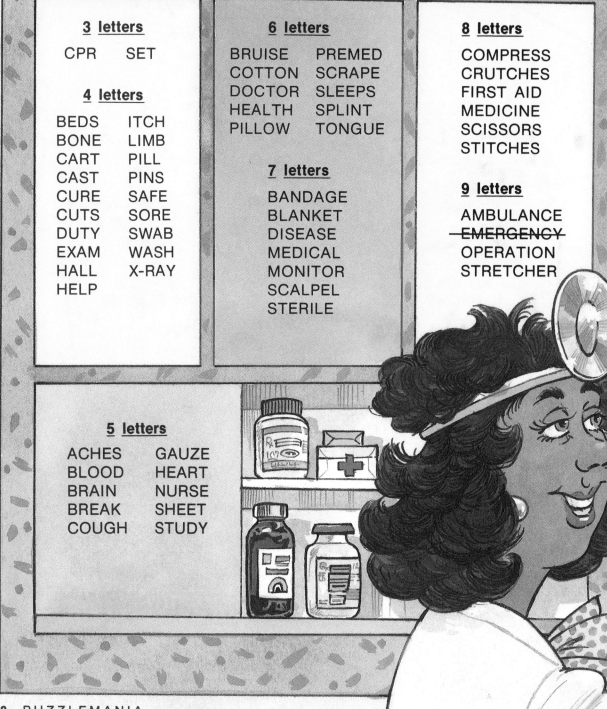

3 letters

CPR   SET

4 letters

BEDS   ITCH
BONE   LIMB
CART   PILL
CAST   PINS
CURE   SAFE
CUTS   SORE
DUTY   SWAB
EXAM   WASH
HALL   X-RAY
HELP

6 letters

BRUISE   PREMED
COTTON   SCRAPE
DOCTOR   SLEEPS
HEALTH   SPLINT
PILLOW   TONGUE

7 letters

BANDAGE
BLANKET
DISEASE
MEDICAL
MONITOR
SCALPEL
STERILE

8 letters

COMPRESS
CRUTCHES
FIRST AID
MEDICINE
SCISSORS
STITCHES

9 letters

AMBULANCE
~~EMERGENCY~~
OPERATION
STRETCHER

5 letters

ACHES   GAUZE
BLOOD   HEART
BRAIN   NURSE
BREAK   SHEET
COUGH   STUDY

EMERGENCY

Answer on page 47.

Illustrated by John Nez

INFINITE FIT

This is the symbol for infinity ∞. It looks like the number 8, but is more stretched out. How many of them can you find hidden in this picture?

Illustrated by R. Michael Palan

PLANET PUP

Can you help Tray-Cee and her dog, Boinker, find their way home?

Answer on page 47.

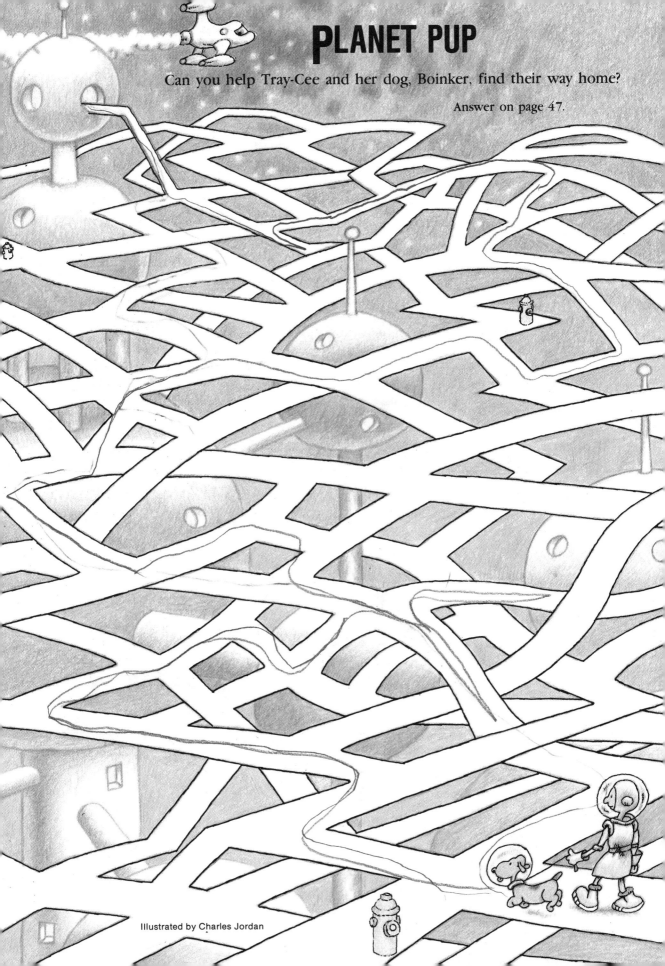

Illustrated by Charles Jordan

MATH CONFUSION

You don't need to be a math whiz to know this puzzle adds up to fun. Divide your attention between these words and the letters on the next page. As you find each word hidden in the grid, subtract it from the list below. Look up, down, across, backward, and diagonally.

	exact	multiplier	quantity	show	
	hard	multiply	radii	subtract	
add	height	odd	same	subtraction	take away
all	into	one	set	sum	ten
and	item	over	short	symbols	times
apiece	less	plus			total
arc	long				two
area	math				value
borrow	minus				
decimal	more				
depth					
divide					

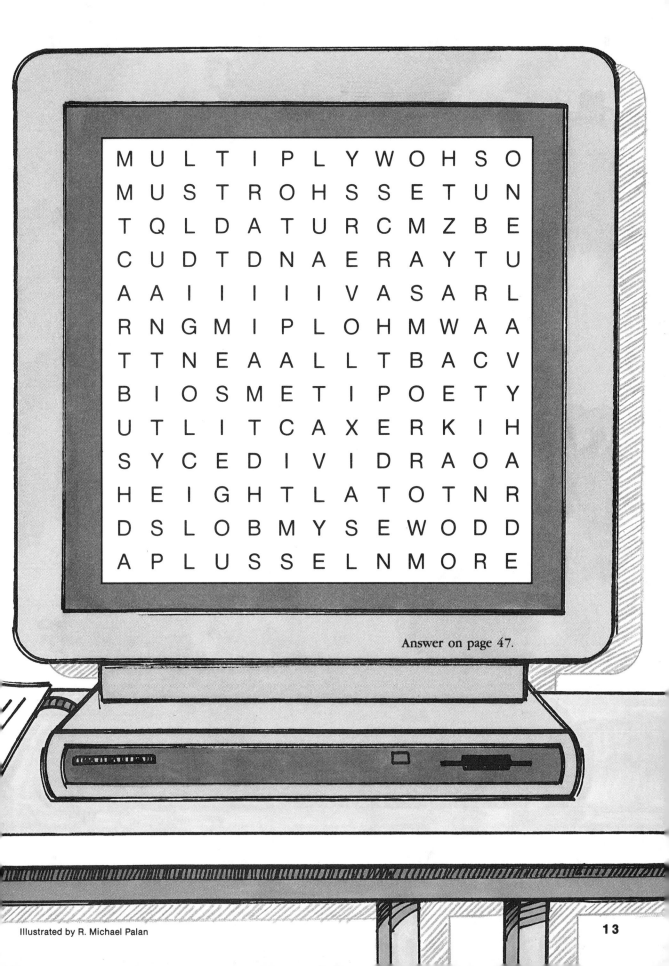

M U L T I P L Y W O H S O
M U S T R O H S S E T U N
T Q L D A T U R C M Z B E
C U D T D N A E R A Y T U
A A I I I I I V A S A R L
R N G M I P L O H M W A A
T T N E A A L L T B A C V
B I O S M E T I P O E T Y
U T L I T C A X E R K I H
S Y C E D I V I D R A O A
H E I G H T L A T O T N R
D S L O B M Y S E W O D D
A P L U S S E L N M O R E

Answer on page 47.

CLOSET CLEANER

Andrea wants to clean this supply closet as a surprise for her mom. On one side of the closet she plans to put all the things used to clean the inside of her house. On the other, she'll put all the outdoor cleaning equipment. Place the name of each pictured item on one of the two lists.

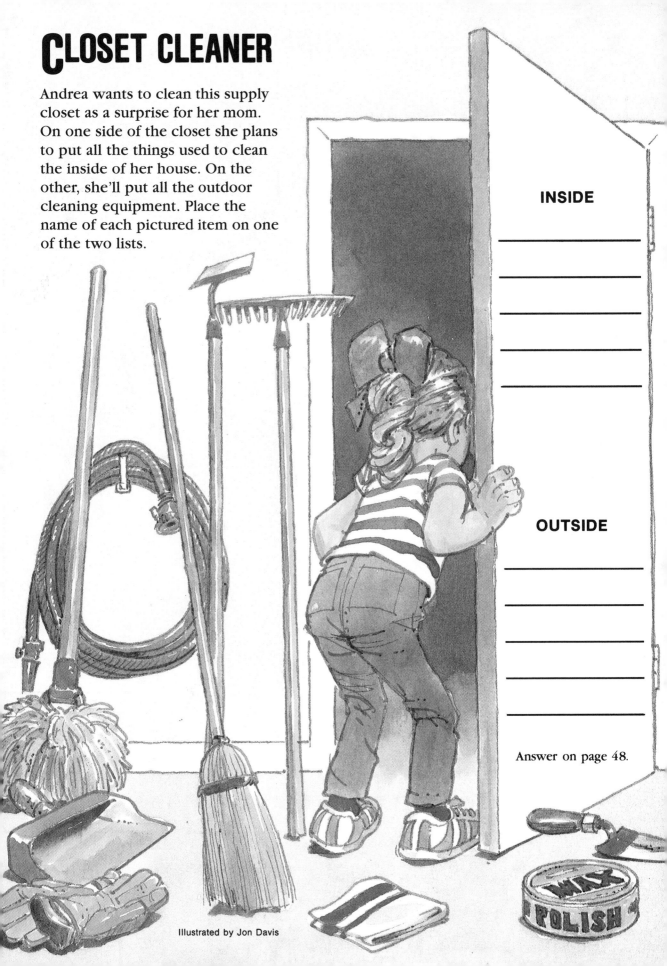

INSIDE

_____

_____

_____

_____

_____

OUTSIDE

_____

_____

_____

_____

_____

Answer on page 48.

Illustrated by Jon Davis

SPELUNKING MEMORIES

Take a long look at this picture. Try to remember everything you see in it. Then turn the page, and try to answer some questions about it without looking back.

DON'T READ THIS UNTIL YOU HAVE LOOKED AT "Spelunking Memories—Part 1" ON PAGE 15.

SPELUNKING MEMORIES
Part 2

Can you answer these questions about the spelunking scene you saw? Don't peek!

1. How many flashlights were on?
2. What were the twins looking at?
3. Who had his canteen out?
4. What ancient pictures were on the wall?
5. How many people were in the cave?
6. What animals were in this cave?
7. Did everyone have a hat on?
8. Who was taking notes?
9. How many people were taking pictures?
10. What was the girl doing with her empty soda pop can?

Answer on page 48.

WHAT ARE YOU?

Use the clues to find the letters that will spell out what you are.

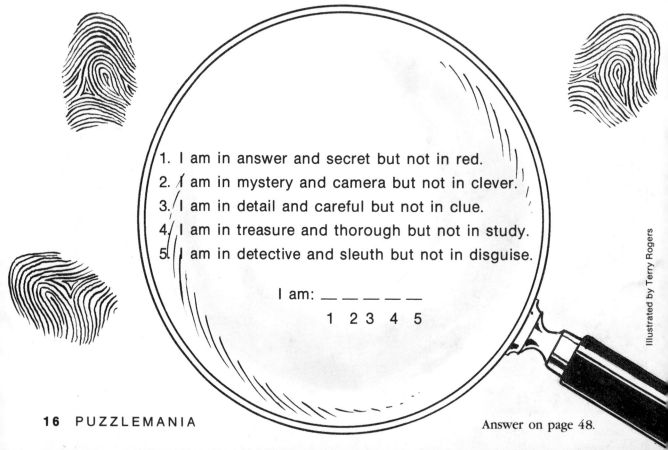

1. I am in answer and secret but not in red.
2. I am in mystery and camera but not in clever.
3. I am in detail and careful but not in clue.
4. I am in treasure and thorough but not in study.
5. I am in detective and sleuth but not in disguise.

I am: _ _ _ _ _
1 2 3 4 5

Illustrated by Terry Rogers

Answer on page 48.

MORE OR LESS

The math club is creating a beautiful quilt for the school auction. It's almost done, but now Ernie has to place one of these symbols: Greater than >, less than <, or equal to =, in the empty squares. He's done a few, but needs your help to fill in the rest. Remember, the open end of the arrow is always toward the larger fraction, while the point is toward the smaller fraction.

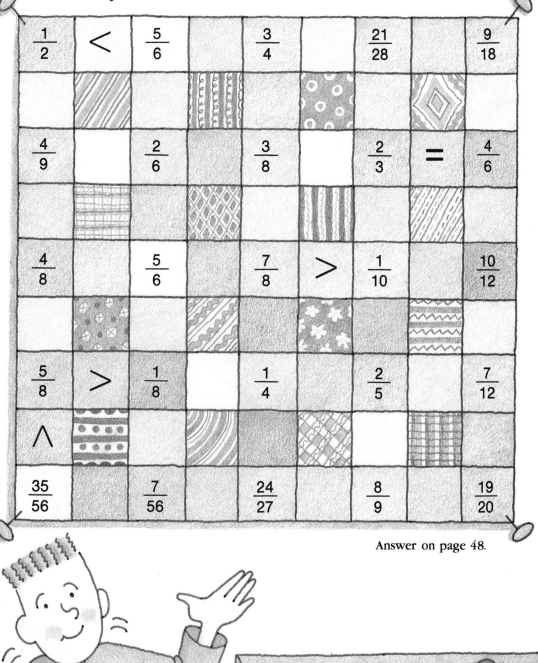

Answer on page 48.

COMMON INTERESTS

Can you tell what thing is shared by all three items in the same group?

Answer on page 48.

1.
duck
baseball cap
diner patron

2.
saw
comb
a person

3.
a grooved plank
a dog
a shoe

4.
needle
hurricane
potato

5.
cuckoo clock
dollar bill
speedometer

6.
fish
music
weight rooms

Illustrated by Anni Matsick

INSTANT PICTURE

To work your way through these snowing dots, fill in
each space that has two dots.

Illustrated by Rob Sepanak

GLOBE PROBE

During a tour of Europe, that world famous adventurer Cincinnati Holmes was followed by all the different breeds of dogs from that continent. After two weeks, he had quite a pack traveling with him. Unfortunately, he couldn't send them back because he couldn't remember which dog came from which country.
Each dog is pictured below next to its country of origin. Help Cincy by writing in the nationality of each dog. Then locate that country on his map.

_____ Malinois

_____ Sheepdog

Fancy Poodle

German Shepherd

Italy Greyhound

Ireland Setter

Wales Corgi

Norway Elkhound

Scotland Deerhound

Answer on page 50.

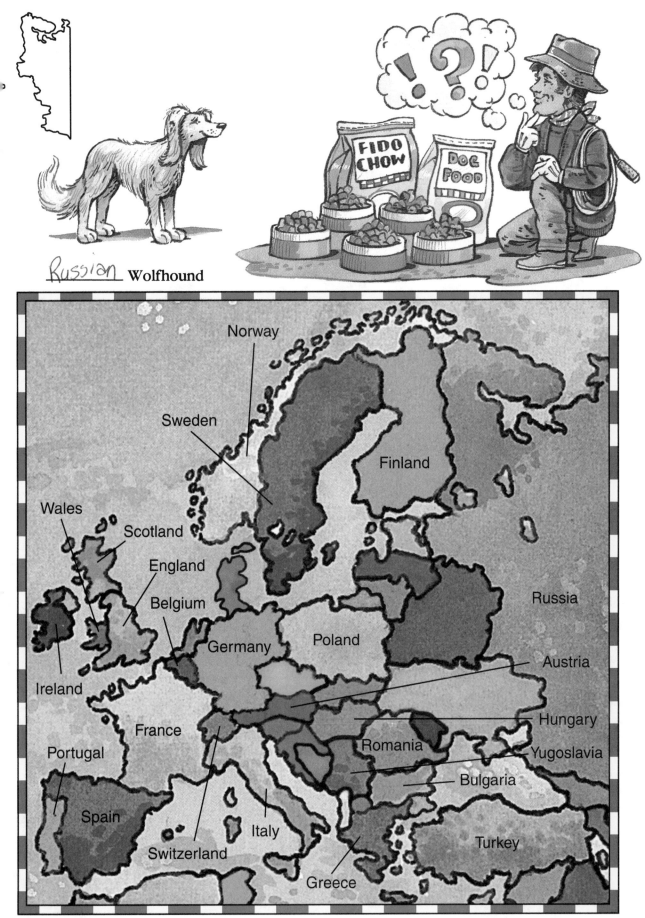

Russian Wolfhound

QUIET QUEST

Be very quiet as you search through this puzzle for words that have silent letters in them. For example, there is COMB. When you say the word "comb," you don't hear a B sound because the B is silent. GHOST is another example, because the H has no sound in this word. How many other words with silent letters can you find?

Marc Nadel

BLANK VERSE

Each poem below can be completed by four words
that rhyme. Can you guess which words go in the blanks?
Each poem has a separate and different set of words.

I promised that I wouldn't _____

About the tinkling silver _____;

My sister dropped it, and it _____

Right to the bottom of the _____.

The little dog was left _____

And howled in a disheartened _____,

"My owner left me just a _____;

I'd rather have an ice-cream _____!"

Illustrated by Barbara Gray

Answer on page 48.

PICTURE MIXER

Copy these mixed-up squares in the spaces on the next page to put this picture back together. The letters and numbers tell you where each square belongs. The first one, A-3, has been done for you.

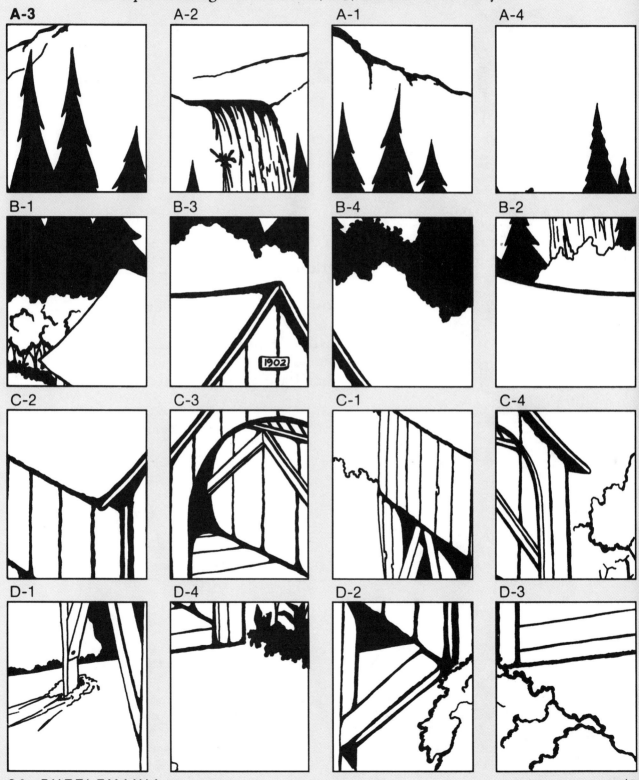

A-3 A-2 A-1 A-4

B-1 B-3 B-4 B-2

C-2 C-3 C-1 C-4

D-1 D-4 D-2 D-3

Answer on page 48.

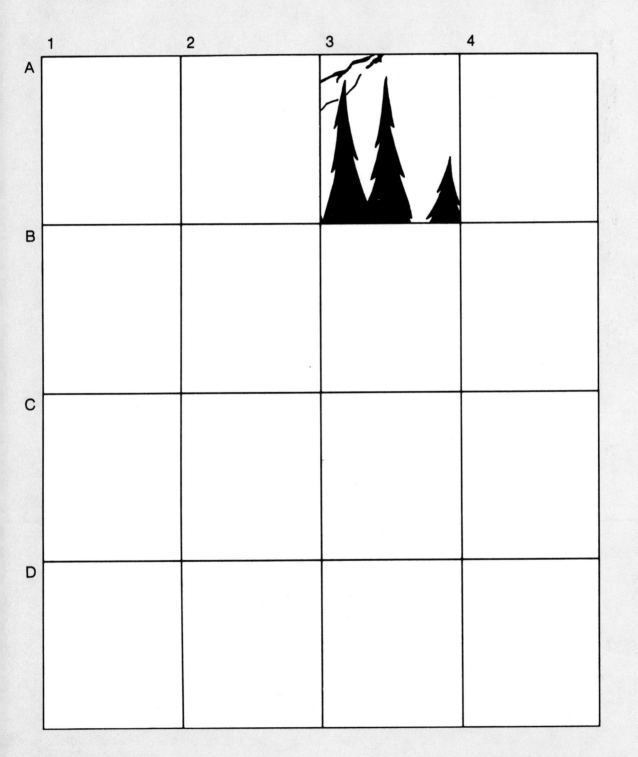

SYMBOL SEARCH

Find the symbol from each line that matches the
symbols in the first column.

Answer on page 48.

26

Illustrated by Richard Johnson

WHAT'S IN A WORD?

When you weatherproof something, you try to keep it from getting too hot or too wet. Well, TOO, HOT, and WET are just three of the many words of three letters or more you can make using some of the letters in WEATHERPROOF. How many more can you find? There are over 100.

Illustrated by Anni Matsick

Answer on page 49.

THE CASE OF THE FRIENDLY FARMER

See if you can solve this mystery. Read the story and fill in the missing words. Then match the numbered letters with the corresponding spaces at the end of the story. If you've filled in the spaces correctly, you'll know what Ralph discovered.

Ralph Rabbit was running a high fever, and his mother said he would have to stay in b e d for a whole week. Doctor's orders! "Oh boy!" thought Ralph, "I won't even have to go to s c h o o l!"

It wasn't any fun, though. Ralph was too sick to w a t c h TV or read comic b o o k s. His head ached, and he couldn't see very clearly. He just stared listlessly out the w i n d o w at the flowers, the elm _ _ _ _ _ , and the b i r d s that flew by.

On the second morning, Ralph noticed a farmer standing in the cornfield across the road. The farmer wore a straw h a t on his head, a plaid s h i r t , and blue overalls. He had his two _ _ _ _ outstretched and was waving to Ralph. What a friendly guy! Ralph waved back weakly, before lying back on his bed and falling fast a l s e e p .

Illustrated by R. Michael Palan

Every morning while he was sick, Ralph _L_ _o_ _o_ _K_ _e_ _d_ out his
9
window to see if the farmer was in the field. He always was, and whenever

Ralph waved, he would see the farmer _W_ _A_ _V_ _e_ right back. It made Ralph
22
feel less lonely, and gradually his high temperature began to come down. Soon

he would be able to go to meet his friend in the _f_ _e_ _i_ _L_ _D_ of corn!
4 2

By the end of the week, Ralph was able to get up. His _L_ _e_ _g_ _S_ were
3
wobbly when he walked, but his fever was gone. Immediately, he put on a warm

_C_ _c_ _t_ ___ and a hat and told his mother, "I'm going over to see a friend."
15
"What friend?" called his mother, but Ralph had already hopped out the

___ ___ ___ ___ .
20
He hurried across the road and into the field. There stood his friend, waiting.

"Hi!" called Ralph as he ran over. Then he stopped in amazement as he

discovered something about his friend.

What did Ralph discover?

___ ___ ___   ___ ___ ___ ___ ___ ___   ___ ___ ___
 1   2   3   4   5   6   7   8   9   10 11 12

___   ___ ___ ___ ___ ___ ___ ___ ___ ___ ___ .
13   14 15 16 17 18 19 20 21 22

Answer on page 49.

ELE-FUN

How many differences can you find between these two pictures?

STOP, LOOK, AND LIST

Under each category, list one thing that begins with every letter. For example, one Wild Cat that begins with "L" is Lynx. See if you can name another.

WILD CATS

L _ion_

T _iger_

C _at (cheetah_

B _obcat_

P _anther_

COLORS

L _avender_

T _an_

C _ream_

B _lue_

P _ink_

TYPES OF MEAT

L _amb_

T _urkey_

C _hikin_

B _eef_

P _ork_

Illustrated by Lisa Dayer

Answer on page 49.

HIDDEN PICTURES

There are at least 30 objects hidden in this picture. How many can you find?

Illustrated by Robert Cuenca

FAMILY REUNION

Bradley Brady went to a family reunion with his parents, Janet and Carl Brady. He met many relatives there. Can you use the clues to help Bradley figure how each person is related?

Clara Clark is Janet's sister.
Kenneth Brady is Carl's brother.
Austin Adams is Janet's father.
Roger Clark is Clara's son.
Austin Adams is Clara's father.
Amanda Clark is Clara's daughter.

1. What is Janet to Roger?
   a. sister b. grandmother c. aunt

2. What is Amanda to Bradley?
   a. sister b. aunt c. cousin

3. What is Bradley to Kenneth?
   a. nephew b. brother c. son

4. What is Roger to Amanda?
   a. cousin b. brother c. grandfather

5. What is Austin Adams to Roger?
   a. father b. grandfather c. uncle

6. What is Bradley to Austin?
   a. grandson b. son c. brother

Answer on page 49.

DOT MAGIC

Can you get a jump on this puzzle by connecting the dots? Hop to it.

Answer on page 49.

Illustrated by Rob Sepanak

PUT ONS

These clues aren't putting you on. Most of them really are about things that can be put on other things. So put on your thinking cap and put the right answers on the right spaces.

Across

1. Put this on a wrapped gift
3. Put it on spaghetti
7. Not ___ I can help it
8. Put this on a hem to hold it in place
9. Abbreviation for average
10. Coming from, going ___
11. Put music on a cassette
13. Put it on the dog
15. Put it around your neck
16. Short for amperage
19. Covering on the table
21. Put it on over a shirt
24. Either ___
25. Abbreviation for Arkansas
26. Center of a hurricane
28. One to avoid in "Tag"
29. Each level of a cake
30. Abbreviation for answer

Down

1. Front of a cap
2. Bottle ___ perfume
3. Spanish for "yes"
4. Tiny insect
5. Put this on a jar or bottle
6. Not odd
8. Hold still for a picture
10. Pin them on the donkey
12. Metal suit a knight puts on
14. Abbreviation for extraterrestrial
16. Plant lotion to put on burns
17. Abbreviation for part-time
18. Egg-shaped
20. Put these on the head
22. Distinct period in time
23. Put the golf ball on it
27. Abbreviation for year
28. Not out

Answer on page 49.

YOUNG ABE

This is a picture of Abraham Lincoln as a teenager. How many things can you find that are wrong or that hadn't been invented when this picture was done?

Illustrated by John Nez

SOUNDS THE SAME

Homonyms are words that sound the same but have different meanings. The blanks in each sentence can be filled in with a homonym of some other word in the same sentence. The first one has been done. See if you can fill in the others.

1. The __TWO__ of us will go, **too.**

2. Which _____ are you, good or bad?

3. That _____ is not tied right.

4. The ants came to my _____ picnic.

5. My son took a _____ bath.

6. Have you the _____ to get to the fair?

7. I picked a rose in one of the _____.

8. I'm _____ at the chess board.

9. I wore my _____ suit to the plane.

10. I _____ prize number one.

Answer on page 50.

FRIGHT SIGHTS

Oh no! Professor Hink Pink's search to find rhymes
has taken him into this haunted house. Now his ghost
host is showing off all the scary things that rhyme.
How many rhymes can you find in these fright sights?

SQUEAK

Illustrated by Terry Rogers

OUT WITH THE TIDE

These ships are ready to shove off, but the harbormaster
didn't cast off their ropes. Untangle this mess by
following the ropes from each pylon to the correct
ship, so it can be untied and sail out to the open sea.

Illustrated by Jerry Zimmerman

Answer on page 50.

A GREAT SKATE

What could be skateboarding down the sidewalk on such a beautiful day? Maybe a sloth hanging four or a scarecrow on a skating tour? Use your imagination to draw in what you think it might be.

A FROG

Illustrated by Paul Richer

THE MORE, THE MERRIER

Each number below stands for a letter of the alphabet. Use the code to discover some special names for things which are found in groups.

A = 16   J = 24   S = 19
B = 20   K = 10   T = 1
C = 12   L = 21   U = 8
D = 23   M = 4   V = 25
E = 3   N = 11   W = 22
F = 26   O = 5   X = 15
G = 14   P = 18   Y = 17
H = 2   Q = 13   Z = 9
I = 7   R = 6

LITTER
21-7-1-1-3-6   *OF* 5-26   *KITTENS* 10-7-1-1-3-11-19

HERD
2-3-6-23   *OF* 5-26   *CATTLE* 12-16-1-1-21-3

T
1-6-5-5-18   *OF* 5-26   14-7-6-21   19-12-5-8-1-19 *T*

OF
12-5-21-5-11-17   5-26   *ANTS* 16-11-1-19

OF
19-12-2-5-5-21   5-26   *PORPOISES* 18-5-6-18-5-7-19-3-19

OF
18-6-7-23-3   5-26   21-7-5-11-19

OF
12-21-8-19-1-3-6   5-26   14-6-16-18-3-19

19-22-16-6-4   5-26   20-3-3-19

18-16-12-10   5-26   22-5-21-25-3-19

12-2-5-6-8-19   5-26   19-7-11-14-3-6-19

26-21-5-12-10   5-26   19-2-3-3-18

20-16-1-12-2   5-26   12-5-5-10-7-3-19

12-5-25-3-17   5-26   13-8-16-7-21

14-16-14-14-21-3   5-26   14-3-3-19-3

20-8-11-12-2   5-26   20-16-11-16-11-16-19

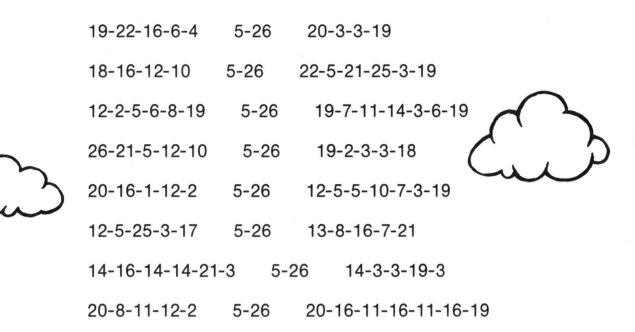

Answer on page 50.

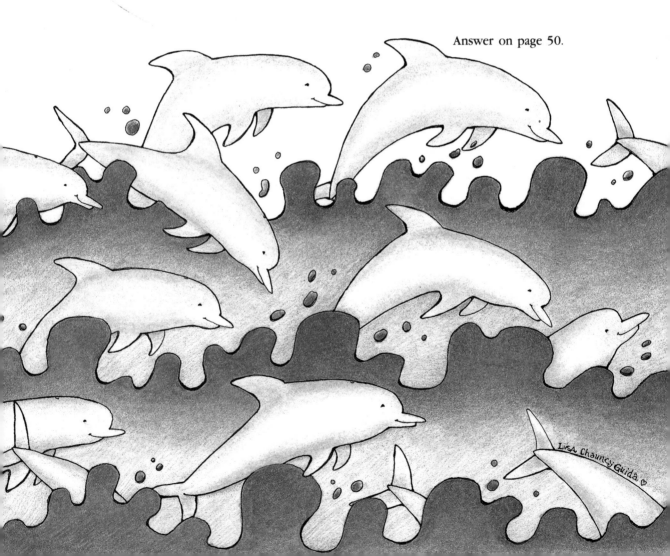

THE FINAL FRONTIER

Can you number these pictures to show what happened first, second, and so on?

Illustrated by Richard Johnson

Answer on page 50.

ANSWERS

SPLIT SCORES (page 3)
These are our answers. You may have found others.

solution	hospital
solo	soil
unit	path

universe	comedian
sure	main
vine	code

triangle	physical
neat	clay
girl	ship

calendar	banister
land	best
race	rain

FOOD FIGHT (pages 4-5)

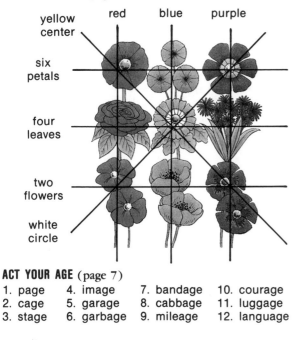

ROW, ROW, ROW (page 6)

ACT YOUR AGE (page 7)

1. page	4. image	7. bandage	10. courage
2. cage	5. garage	8. cabbage	11. luggage
3. stage	6. garbage	9. mileage	12. language

HOSPITAL HAPPENINGS (pages 8-9)

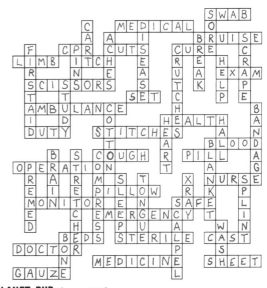

PLANET PUP (page 11)

MATH CONFUSION (pages 12-13)

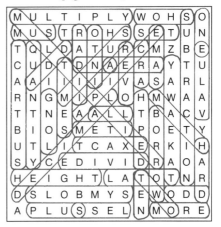

CLOSET CLEANER (page 14)

INSIDE	OUTSIDE
polish	hose
dustpan	trowel
mop	hoe
broom	rake
towel	gloves

SPELUNKING MEMORIES (page 16)

1. Two
2. A stalactite
3. Steve
4. A fire and a mammoth
5. Seven
6. Bats and a frog
7. No, Steve had taken his hat off.
8. Nancy
9. One
10. Putting it in her backpack to take out with her.

WHAT ARE YOU? (page 16)

I am: s m a r t
      1̄ 2̄ 3̄ 4̄ 5̄

MORE OR LESS (page 17)

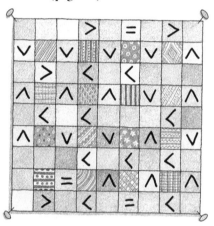

COMMON INTERESTS (page 18)

1. a bill
2. teeth
3. a tongue
4. an eye
5. numbers
6. scales

INSTANT PICTURE (page 19)

GLOBE PROBE (pages 20-21)

This answer appears on page 50.

BLANK VERSE (page 23)

I promised that I wouldn't TELL
About the tinkling silver BELL;
My sister dropped it, and it FELL
Right to the bottom of the WELL.

The little dog was left ALONE
And howled in a disheartened TONE,
"My owner left me just a BONE;
I'd rather have an ice-cream CONE!"

PICTURE MIXER (pages 24-25)

SYMBOL SEARCH (page 26)

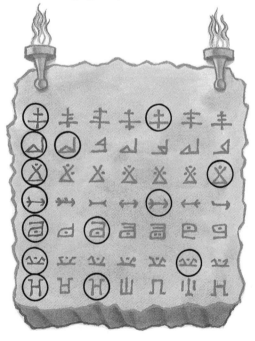

WHAT'S IN A WORD (page 27)

These are the words we found. You may have found others.

after	few	hoe	pear	report	tower
ape	foot	hoof	peat	reproof	trap
are	for	hoofer	peer	roar	tree
art	fore	hoop	pert	roof	war
ate	fort	hop	peter	roofer	ware
awe	forth	hope	poof	rope	warp
ear	free	how	poor	rot	wart
earth	fret	oaf	pore	rote	water
eat	froth	oar	port	row	wear
era	hare	oat	pot	tape	weather
ether	harp	opera	power	taper	were
ewe	hart	operate	proof	tar	what
far	hat	orate	raft	tarp	wheat
fare	hate	ore	rap	tea	where
farther	hear	other	rat	tear	woof
fat	heart	owe	rate	thaw	woofer
fate	heat	par	rather	the	worth
father	heater	pare	raw	there	wrap
fear	her	parrot	reap	three	wrath
feather	herd	part	reef	throw	wreath
feet	here	pat	reefer	top	wreathe
fete	hew	path	repeat	tor	wrote

THE CASE OF THE FRIENDLY FARMER (pages 28-29)

Ralph Rabbit was running a high fever, and his mother said he would have to stay in BED for a whole week. Doctor's orders! "Oh boy!" thought Ralph, "I won't even have to go to SCHOOL!"

It wasn't any fun, though. Ralph was too sick to WATCH TV or read comic BOOKS. His head ached, and he couldn't see very clearly. He just stared listlessly out the WINDOW at the flowers, the elm TREES, and the BIRDS that flew by.

On the second morning, Ralph noticed a farmer standing in the cornfield across the road. The farmer wore a straw HAT on his head, a plaid SHIRT, and blue overalls. He had his two ARMS outstretched and was waving to Ralph. What a friendly guy! Ralph waved back weakly, before lying back on his bed and falling fast ASLEEP.

Every morning while he was sick, Ralph LOOKED out his window to see if the farmer was in the field. He always was, and whenever Ralph waved, he would see the farmer WAVE right back. It made Ralph feel less lonely, and gradually his high temperature began to come down. Soon he would be able to go to meet his friend in the FIELD of corn!

By the end of the week, Ralph was able to get up. His LEGS were wobbly when he walked, but his fever was gone. Immediately, he put on a warm COAT and a hat and told his mother, "I'm going over to see a friend."

"What friend?" called his mother, but Ralph had already hopped out the DOOR.

He hurried across the road and into the field. There stood his friend, waiting. "Hi!" called Ralph as he ran over. Then he stopped in amazement as he discovered something about his friend.

```
H I S   F R I E N D   W A S
1 2 3   4 5 6 7 8 9   10 11 12
A   S C A R E C R O W .
13  14 15 16 17 18 19 20 21 22
```

STOP, LOOK, AND LIST (page 31)

These are our answers. You may have found others.

Wild Cats	**Colors**
Lion	Lavender
Tiger	Tan
Cheetah	Cream
Bobcat	Blue
Panther	Pink

Types of Meat
Lamb
Turkey
Chicken
Beef
Pork

FAMILY REUNION (page 34)

1. c   4. b
2. c   5. b
3. a   6. a

DOT MAGIC (page 35)

PUT ONS (pages 36-37)

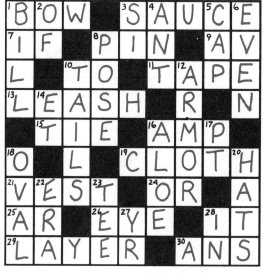

SOUNDS THE SAME (page 39)

1. two
2. witch
3. knot
4. aunt's
5. sun
6. fare
7. rows
8. bored
9. plain
10. won

FRIGHT SIGHTS (pages 40-41)

The professor is wearing his letter sweater, eye tie, and blue shoes.
The rhymes being shown by the ghost host include:
frightening lightning
squeaker sneaker
pants dance
book hook
fat bat
scary canary
rich witch
hobbling goblin
dead Fred
scare chair
bone phone
mummy tummy
moose noose
lime slime
black crack

GLOBE PROBE (pages 20-21)

1. <u>Belgian</u> Malinois
2. <u>English</u> Sheepdog
3. <u>French</u> Poodle
4. <u>German</u> Shepherd
5. <u>Italian</u> Greyhound
6. <u>Irish</u> Setter
7. <u>Welsh</u> Corgi
8. <u>Norwegian</u> Elkhound
9. <u>Scottish</u> Deerhound
10. <u>Russian</u> Wolfhound

OUT WITH THE TIDE (page 42)

1. A   3. B
2. D   4. C

THE MORE, THE MERRIER (pages 44-45)

Litter of Kittens
Herd of Cattle
Troop of Girl Scouts
Colony of Ants
School of Porpoises
Pride of Lions
Cluster of Grapes
Swarm of Bees
Pack of Wolves
Chorus of Singers
Flock of Sheep
Batch of Cookies
Covey of Quail
Gaggle of Geese
Bunch of Bananas

THE FINAL FRONTIER (page 46)

3   6
5   2
1   4

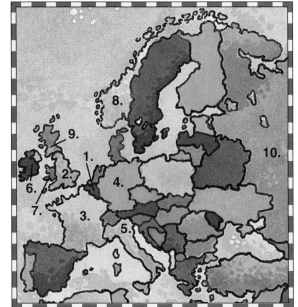

Editor: Jeffrey A. O'Hare • **Art Director:** Timothy J. Gillner
Project Director: Pamela Gallo • **Editorial Consultant:** Andrew Gutelle
Design Consultant: Bob Feldgus

Puzzle Contributors
Karen Anderson • Barbara Backer • Diane Cheffy • Debbie Driscoll
Evelyn Furey • Phillis Henry • Kathleen Pestotnik Iverson • Virginia Kroll
Rich Latta • Jo Mason • Bernard Traciak • Kathy Trupp
Milly Osvold Wells • Arleen Wixtrom